MUSIC LIBRARY			

782:81

878,667

SOUTH TYNESIDE LIBRARIES

The last date entered is the date by which the book must be returned, and fines will be charged if the book is kept after this date.

Changes of address should be notified immediately.

Printed in England by Commercial Colour Press, London E.7.

THE BOY FRIEND

A New Musical Comedy
of the 1920's

BOOK, LYRICS AND MUSIC BY

SANDY WILSON

PUBLISHED BY

CHAPPELL & CO., LTD.,

50 NEW BOND STREET, LONDON, W.1

Time: 1926

ACT I
The Drawing Room of the Villa Caprice,
Madame Dubonnet's Finishing School, Near Nice.

Morning

———

INTERVAL

———

ACT II
The Plage

Afternoon

———

INTERVAL

———

ACT III
The Terrasse of the Café Pataplon

Night

"The Boy Friend" was originally presented at the Players' Theatre on 14th April, 1953. The first public presentation was at Wyndhams Theatre on 14th January, 1954, when the cast was as follows:

HORTENSE (*a French Maid*)		VIOLETTA
MAISIE	*Pupils at Mme. Dubonnet's Finishing School*	DENISE HIRST
DULCIE		MARIA CHARLES
FAY		JOAN GADSDON
NANCY		JULIET HUNT
POLLY BROWNE		ANNE ROGERS
MARCEL		STEPHEN WARWICK
PIERRE		JACK THOMSON
ALPHONSE		GEOFFREY WEBB
MADAME DUBONNET		JOAN STERNDALE BENNETT
BOBBY VAN HUSEN		LARRY DREW
PERCIVAL BROWNE		HUGH PADDICK
TONY		ANTHONY HAYES
LORD BROCKHURST		JOHN RUTLAND
LADY BROCKHURST		BERYL COOKE
GENDARME		HUGH FORBES
A WAITER		ALAN DUDLEY
PÉPÉ	*Speciality Dancers*	STEPHEN WARWICK
LOLITA		JOAN GADSDON
GUESTS		STELLA CHAPMAN
		ELEANOR McCREADY
		ROBERT HARGREAVES

The part of Percival Browne was taken over in
May 1954 by Fred Stone

PRODUCED BY VIDA HOPE

Dances arranged by John Heawood

Scenery and costumes by Reginald Woolley

THE BOY FRIEND

MUSICAL CONTENTS

THE BOY FRIEND

SANDY WILSON

No 1

OVERTURE

Piano

Bright

A

B

44762

MADE IN ENGLAND

Valse con moto

Chappell

E Moderato *(rhythmically in 4)*

G Moderato, not too fast *(in 4)*

Chappell

Act I

Nº 2

CHORUS OF GIRLS–(with Solo–Hortense)

"PERFECT YOUNG LADIES"

Note:– At curtain rise Piano (only) plays from 1st bar ad lib (under dialogue) till Cue

Cue: (GIRLS) "Of course not"

Chappell

Dialogue
Chappell

No 3   ENSEMBLE—(Polly, Dulcie, Fay, Maisie, Girls and Boys)

"THE BOY FRIEND"

Cue: (GIRLS) Oh, do tell us about him, Polly!

Moderato   **A little faster**

(POLLY) Well, there really isn't very much to tell. I expect you know how I feel as well as I do.

pp (under dialogue)   *leggiero*

Polly

An-y girl who's reached the age Of sev-en-teen or there-a-bouts Has but one de-

-sire in view. ____ She knows she has reached the stage Of

need-ing one to care a-bout; No-thing else will real-ly do. ____

Chappell

E **Boys**

Life with-out us is im-poss-i-ble And de-void_ of all charms.

No a-mount of i-dle goss-ip-'ll Keep them out_ of our arms. *(in 4)*

Slowly *(in 4)*
Polly & Girls

We're blue_ with-out Can't do_ with-out Our dreams just won't come true with-out

That cer-tain thing called the Boy Friend. **Tempo I** *(in 2)*

Chappell

DANCE

Ensemble

We're blue_ with-out   Can't do_ with out   Our dreams just won't come true with-out

That cer - tain thing called the Boy Friend._____

(Dialogue)

№4　　　MADAME DUBONNET'S ENTRANCE

Cue: (MAISIE) "Cave, girls, here's Madame Dubonnet"

Moderato　　(*Madame D. sings melody, without words*)

(Dialogue)

Chappell

N⁰ 5

DUET (Bobby and Maisie)

"WON'T YOU CHARLESTON?"

Cue: MAISIE. Really, I don't believe it.

Charleston tempo

Bobby

List - en, ba - by, __ to my __ plea; Won't you come danc - ing with me? __ Be my __ ba - by, __ and say __ yes. Or else I'm done for, I guess. __

Chappell

 Chappell

Chappell

Chappell

18

(Segue after applause)

Chappell

No 5a

REPRISE—(Bobby and Maisie)
"WON'T YOU CHARLESTON?"

Faster

Both

Won't you — Charles-ton — with me? — Won't you —

Charles - ton — with me? — And while the band is play-ing that

Old vo-de-o-do. A-round we will go,

To-geth-er we'll show them How the__ Charles-ton__ is done.__

We'll sur - prise ev - 'ry - one.__ Just think what Hea - ven

it's going to be If you will Charles-ton, Charles-ton, Charles-ton,

If you will Charles-ton, Charles-ton__ with me!__

ff
(Drums ad lib.)

(Dialogue)
Chappell

<u>N°. 6</u>

DUET— (Madame Dubonnet and Percival)

"FANCY FORGETTING"

Cue: Mme. DUBONNET "Let me see, how did it go?"

Chappell

22

44762   Chappell

-mem-ber it too, Fan-cy, just fan-cy you for - get - ting.

C DANCE

D Both

Though the years go by, And our youth is gone, Mem-o-ries don't die, Like a

rall.   *a tempo*

song they lin-ger on. So just when I thought you'd re - mem-ber it too,

rall.   *a tempo*

Fan - cy, just fan - cy you for - get - ting.

Fan - cy, just fan - cy you for - get - ting.

Dialogue

№ 7

MELOS
POLLY'S LETTER

Cue: (POLLY) "Good-bye" (Girls exuent)

Moderato *(in 4)*

(Polly throws letter)

Tony enters - Dialogue

Chappell

DUET—(Tony and Polly)

* "I COULD BE HAPPY WITH YOU"

Cue: (TONY) "I think you're terribly"— (POLLY) "Yes?"

I don't claim that I am psy-chic, But one look at you and I kick A-

(Orch. tacet Voice and Piano only)

-way ev-'ry scru-ple I learnt as a pu-pil In school, my dear.

I'm not one to make pre-dict-ions, But I've thrown off all re-strict-ions And

44762

Chappell

POL: don't mind con-fess-ing I think it's a bless-ing That you are here.

Tony

Though I'm pre - pared to find I'm wrong, _____ I've got a fun - ny

TONY: feel - ing we be - long To - geth - er. I could be hap-py with

TONY: you _____ If you could be hap - py with me. _____

Polly

TONY: I'd be con - tent-ed to live an - y - where, _____

Chappell

 Chappell

Chappell

Chappell

live an-y-where, What would I care. As long as

you were there? Skies may not al-ways be blue, But one thing is

clear as can be._____ I know that I could be hap-py with

you, My darl-ing, If you could be hap-py with me.

Dialogue

Chappell

FINALE- ACT I
REPRISE (Ensemble)
"THE BOY FRIEND"

Cue: (POLLY) "He's really arrived!"

Life with-out us is im-poss-i-ble And de-void of all

charms. No a-mount of i-dle goss-ip-'ll Keep them out of our

arms.

Slowly (in 4)

(in 4)

We're blue with-out Can't do with-out Our dreams just

won't come true with-out That cer-tain thing called the Boy Friend.

End of Act I

Chappell

1st INTERMISSION

C Meno mosso

D

Broadly

Faster (*in 2*)

Segue

Chappell

Act II

ENSEMBLE
"SUR LE PLAGE"

Tempo di Marcia

Ensemble

A

ENS: love - ly day ___ What a love - ly day ___ For a

ENS: dip in the sea. ___ Oh, what fun

ENS: it will be! ___ Won't you come and have a swim with

Chappell

Chappell

38

44762

Chappell

Chappell

DANCE

Chappell

Chappell

DUET – (Tony and Polly)

"A ROOM IN BLOOMSBURY"

Cue: (TONY) "How ripping — So am I!"

Moderato

Tony A

A life of wealth does not ap-peal to me at all Do you a-

-gree at all? **Polly** I do. **Tony** The mere i-dea of liv-ing in a

44762

Chappell

Polly

Tony

pa - lace is So full of fal - la - cies. That's true. I've

got a ve - ry diff - 'rent sort of scheme in mind, It's just a

dream de - signed For two. Would you care to hear a -

Polly *rall.*

- bout it, dear? Would I care to? Can you doubt it, dear?

B *a tempo*

1 (TONY) All I want is a room   In Blooms — bu — ry,
2 (POLLY) All we want is a room   In Blooms — bu — ry,

mf a tempo

Just a room that will   do   For you   and me.   One room's e —
Just a room that will   do   For you   and me.   I'll sew the

—nough for us,   Though it's   on the top   floor.   Life may   be
cov — ers for   Two   old co — sy arm — chairs.   Neigh — bours   will

rough for us,   But its trou — bles we'll ig — nore.   On a win — ter — y
love us for   We shall laugh at   all our cares.   (TONY) While I'm read — ing a

C

night   I'll   light   a   fire.   Ev-'ry-thing I shall   do As
book. (POLLY)I'll   cook   a   stew.   Then I'll bake a plum duff E-

you   de - sire.   (POLLY)You'll be sit-ting (TONY)And you'll be knit-ting And
-nough   for   two.   (BOTH)In   our   at - tic   We'll be ec -sta-tic As

so con - tent - ed we'll be   In our dear lit - tle   room in Blooms-bu-
love birds up — in a tree.   All we want is a   room in Blooms-bu-

1
- ry.

2
- ry.

Chappell

D DANCE

p staccato

marc. la melodia

R.H.

E

staccato

f

Both

All we want is a   room in Blooms-bu – ry. _____

44762

Segue at cue:-
Tony hand in pocket for key
Chappell

Chappell

№ 13

SONG — (Hortense) with Ensemble
"IT'S NICER IN NICE"

Note:– *The orchestral parts are in* 2/4 *time*

Cue: (HORTENSE) "And I'm very proud of it, too."

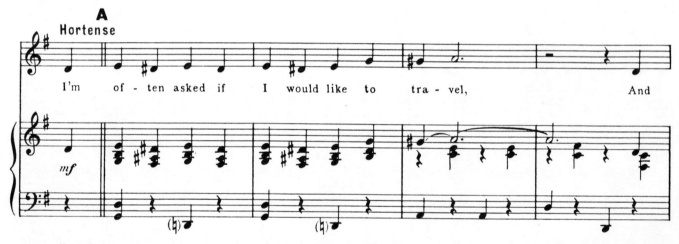

I'm of-ten asked if I would like to tra-vel, And

vi-sit oth-er lands a-cross the sea, _____ But

Chappell

though it might be plea-sant, I think that, for the pre-sent, This

is the place where I pre-fer to be. _____ Let

oth-ers go to Swe-den or Si-am, _____ I

think I'll stay ex-act-ly where I am. _____ **1** They

50

44762   Chappell

dal - liance, And they're al - so keen on it in Greece. But what-
-cut - ta, But they might have trou-ble with the p'lice. Oh, la, la! Oth - er

- ev - er they may say, This is where I want to stay, For it's so much
pla - ces may be fun, But when all is said and done It is so much

Ensemble

She says it's ni - cer, much ni - cer in Nice.

ni - cer in Nice.
ni - cer in

She says it's ni - cer, much ni - cer in Nice.

2 Some Nice.

Chappell

Chappell

Hortense _pp_

But they might have trou - ble with the P'lice! Oh, mon Dieu! Tho' I know a love af - fair is de - lic - ious an - y - where, It is So much ni - cer in Nice! And

Chappell

E

some may like a flut-ter In Bom-bay or Cal-cut-ta, But they might have

(S/A) some may like a flut-ter In Bom-bay or Cal-cut-ta, But they might have

trou-ble with the p'lice. Oth-er pla-ces may be fun, But when

(S/A) trou-ble with the p'lice. Oth-er pla-ces may be fun, But when

Chappell

all is said and done It is so much ni - cer So much

all is said and done It is so much ni - cer

ni - cer So much ni - cer in Nice!_____

So much ni - cer in Nice!_____

Dialogue

Chappell

Nº 14

SONG—(Madame Dubonnet and Percival)

"THE 'YOU-DON'T-WANT-TO-PLAY-WITH-ME' BLUES"

Cue: (PERCIVAL) "Yes, most definitely"

Blues tempo

Mme. Dubonnet *(spoken ad lib)*

Per - cy, Per - cy, Please have mer - cy.

a tempo (Sung)

Why must you al - ways be so sad and gloom-y? Why can't you be a lit - tle

A *(Sung)*

nic - er to me? Ché - ri, Ché - ri, Please be mer - ry,

(a tempo)   *rall.*

When I am try-ing to be bright and jol - ly It is - n't nice to be so mel - an - cho - ly.

Chappell

B

Chappell

Mme DUB: At spread-ing mirth and joy. ___ But it's no good

Mme DUB: With such a sul-ky boy. ___ I try To play the game the oth-er

Mme DUB: fel-lows all choose: _____ I sigh Be-cause you al-ways re-fuse.

Percival: The oth-er fel-lows all choose

Mme DUB: What is a girl to do

Chappell

Mme. Dubonnet

What is a girl to do

All

With such a boy as you? I've got those Drea - ry, Wea - ry,

rall. Mme. Dubonnet **Slower** All

You-don't-want-to-play-with-me blues.__ I've got those Drea - ry,

rall.

Wea - ry, You-don't-want-to-play-with-me blues.__

Dialogue

44762 Chappell

Nº 15

SONG—(Maisie and Boys)
"SAFETY IN NUMBERS"

Note:- The orchestral parts are in $\frac{2}{4}$ time

Cue: (BOBBY) "Listen to me"

Chappell

Chappell

C *2nd time–* **Boys**

MAI

p-f

safe - ty_____ in num - bers,_____ That's what I_____

MAI

_____ be - lieve,_____ The girl who knows_____ A

MAI

lot of beaux_____ Is nev - er like - ly to grieve._____

D

MAI

_____ The la - dy_____ who slum - bers_____ Is

Chappell

left high_____ and dry._____ But I'm a-wake_ _____ And nev - er miss_____ The chance to take_____ An - -oth - er kiss._____ There's safe - ty_____ in num - bers_____ _____ And the more the mer - ri - er am I._____ There's

1   Boys

Chappell

Maisie & Boys

marcato

cresc.   *al fine*

sffz

col 8va ....

sffz

Dialogue

Chappell

№ 16

FINALE—ACT II

Cue: (POLLY) "What did I say?"

Chappell

one thing is clear as can be, _____ I know that I could be

Both

Stop

hap-py with you, My dar-ling, If you could be hap-py with .....

(Orch.)

(Dialogue continues)

No 16ª

Cue: (POLLY) "A thief! Oh, no,"

Andante moderato

pp (under dialogue)

8va ---------- loco

Stop

(Fade)

(Dialogue
continues)

Cue: (HORTENSE) "I think I can explain" ····

····"That men was Monsieur···   (POLLY) No! Hortense! You promised! (Mme. DUB) But what is it Polly?"

(POLLY) It's nothing, Madame, I'm just a little disappointed that's all. You see, I shan't be going to the Carnival Ball after all

№ 16c

Polly

I could be hap-py with you,___ If you could be

hap-py with me.___ I'd be con-ten-ted to

live an-y-where___ What could I care,___ As long as you were there?

Chappell

Ensemble

Skies may not al-ways be blue, _____ But one thing is clear as can be, _____ I know that I could be hap-py with you, My dar-ling, If you could be hap-py with me. Hap-py with me!

End of Act II

Chappell

№ 17

2ND INTERMISSION

In Bright 4

Timp. *f*

Chappell

C Fast *(in 2)*

(Orch. parts are in 2/4)

Segue

44762

Chappell

OPENING ACT III

Stop at Cue:(PIERRE) "Regardez, regardez.... Mme. Dubonnet"

Chappell

Nᵒ 18ᵃ

Cue: (LORD B.) "That's a familiar word"

Valse moderato

pp (under dialogue)

Fade at Cue: (Mme. DUBONNET) "Have some Champagne"

1 (Optional)

2

Chappell

No 18ᵇ

Cue: (PERCIVAL) "For that I shall always be grateful"

Valse moderato

Stop at Cue: (Mme. DUBONNET) "You said"

Chappell

Nº 18c

Cue: (PERCIVAL) "Yes! I'm beginning to remember"

Valse moderato

(Dialogue)

Nº 19

DUET — (Bobby and Maisie) with Chorus
"THE RIVIERA"

Cue: (BOYS) "How?"

(BOBBY) "We can ＿ ＿

Bright tempo

Dance All "Yes!"

Bobby & Maisie

When trou-ble trou-bles you, The on-ly thing to do ＿ Is

dance, you sim-ply got-ta dance. ＿＿＿＿＿

Chappell

Boys & Girls

And if you've had a tiff,— You'll soon for - get it, if— You

dance, you sim-ply got-ta dance._____

Here in the South of France They've got a new step._____

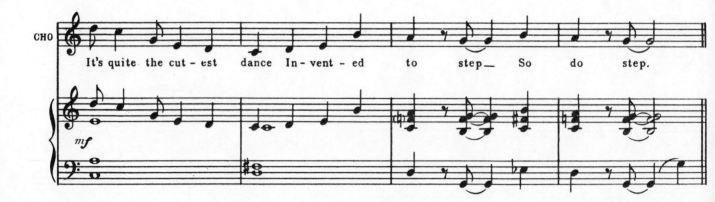

It's quite the cut - est dance In - vent - ed to step— So do step.

A Girls
Wrig-gle your hips and kick up your heels, You'll be sur-prised how love-ly it feels.

All
Ev - 'ry-bod - y's do-ing the Riv - i - er - a.

Boys
Wig-gle your fin-gers wag-gle your toes, Just how it start - ed no-bod - y knows,

All
Ev - 'ry-bod-y's do-ing the Riv-i - er - a.

Chappell

Mul - ti - mill - ion - aires and their lit - tle pets do it.

Ev - en maid - en la - dies who wear lorg - nettes Have tak - en to it

Tell ev - 'ry - one to give out the news. This is the way to shake off the blues.

Ev - 'ry - bod - y's do - ing the Riv - i - er - a!

Chappell

DANCE

Tell ev-'ry-one to give out the news. This is the way to shake off the blues. Ev-'ry-bod-y's do-ing the Riv-i — er — a! —

D

All the bright young things and their bright young beaux do it.

Ev - en duch-ess - es and their gig-o - los Have tak - en to it.

Ain't it ter-rif - ic? Ain't it the top? You got - ta dance right on till you drop.

Ev - 'ry - bod - y's do-ing the Riv-i - er - a!

Chappell

DANCE

(Segue after applause)

Chappell

Nº 19ª

REPRISE
"THE RIVIERA"

L'istesso tempo

Get on the dance floor, get in the swing, This is the time for hav-ing a fling.

Ev - 'ry - bod - y's do-ing the Riv - i - er - a.

Clap-a your hands and slap on your thighs, Grin like a goon and roll up your eyes,

Ev - 'ry - bod - y's do-ing the Riv - i - er - a.

86

All the bright young things and their bright young beaux do it.

Ev - en duch - ess — es and their gig - o — los Have tak - en to it.

Ain't it ter - rif - ic? Ain't it the top? You got - ta dance right on till you drop.

Ev - 'ry - bod - y's do - ing the Riv - i — er — a!

(Chord for applause)

(Almost Segue)

44762

Chappell

No 20
TONY'S ENTRANCE

Cue: (HORTENSE) "Oh! Champagne!"

No 20ª
TONY'S DANCE

Cue: (HORTENSE) "She may not come at all" (*Exit*)

Chappell

Nº 21

DUET—(Lord Brockhurst and Dulcie)
"IT'S NEVER TOO LATE TO FALL IN LOVE"

Cue: (LORD BROCKHURST) "Yes, like me for instance"

44762

Chappell

 Chappell

Dulcie

Boop - a - doop, Boop - a - doop, Boop - a - doop.

love. It's nev-er too late to

wink an eye, I'll do it un - til the day I die, And it's

Boop - a - doop, Boop-a - doop, Boop-a-doop.

nev-er too late to fall in love. If

Chappell

Lord B. they say I'm too old for you, Then I shall an-swer "Why, Sir, One

DUL. nev - er drinks the wine that's new; The old wine tastes much nic - er:" A

Lord B. gent-le-man nev-er feels too weak To pat a pink arm or pinch a cheek, And it's

DUL. Sez who? Sez you?

Lord B. nev-er too late to fall in love. Sez me Sez

Chappell

Chappell

DUL. nev-er too late to flirt and spoon ... And it's

Lord B. A fid-dle that's old is more in tune,

DUL. nev-er too late to fall in love ... The

Lord B. Whack-a - do, Whack-a - do, Whack-a - do.

DUL. mod-ern ar - tists of to - day May paint their pic - ture fast-er, But

when it comes to skill, I say You can't beat an old mas-ter! It's

never too late to bill and coo, At an-y age one and one make two And it's

never too late to fall in, never too late to fall in,

never too late to fall in love! _____

Segue after applause

Chappell

REPRISE
"IT'S NEVER TOO LATE TO FALL IN LOVE"

L'istesso tempo

Dulcie: It's nev-er too late to blow a kiss Es-

Dul: -pec-ial-ly at a time like this And it's nev-er too late to fall in

Dulcie: Vo - de - o, Vo - de - o, Vo - de - o.

Lord B.: love. It's nev- er too late for

Chappell

Lord B. I am sure that you'll a - gree A ru - in— Can be charm - ing It's

DUL. nev - er too late to be a beau, Ex - pe - ri-ence counts a lot, you know And it's

Both nev - er too late to fall in, nev - er too late to fall in,

Both nev - er too late to fall in love. ____

(Dialogue)
Chappell

Nº 22

CARNIVAL TANGO

Cue: (LADY BROCKHURST) "Revolting!"

Chappell

(Dialogue)
Chappell

No 23   DUET—(Madame Dubonnet and Polly)

"POOR LITTLE PIERRETTE"

Cue: (Mme. DUBONNET) "Yes, I think so"

Mme. Dubonnet

There is an old French leg - end That's set to an old French tune. It

tells how Pier - rot loved Pier - rette Un - der a sum - mer moon.

Ev - 'ry night the lov - ers meet Just as the clock strikes nine.

44762

Chappell

Mme. DUB

Then he gives her kis - ses sweet As vint - age wine.

Mme. DUB

But, a - las, one fate - ful night Pier - rette is for - sworn.

(Orch. enters)

pp

Mme. DUB

There she stands for - lorn Till the cold grey dawn.

rall.

A **With feeling** (*not too slow*)

Mme. DUB

Poor lit - tle Pier - rette, Where's your Pier - rot?

a tempo

Chappell

Polly (2nd Verse only)

Ah _____

Why are you all a - lone? _____

Ah _____

You should be So fan-cy free, Your heart should be high. _____

Ah _____

But in-stead You hang your head And try not to cry. _____

poco rall.

Chappell

then He may come back a - gain.

then He may come back a - gain.

C Poco più mosso

Poor lit - tle Pier - rette, Where's your Pier - rot?

Poor lit - tle Pier - rette, Where's your Pier - rot?

Why are you all a - lone? _____

Why are you all a - lone? _____

Chappell

Chappell

Your dream of love has flown._____

Your dream of love has flown._____

Just keep on danc - ing Till the dawn, and then

Just keep on danc - ing Till the dawn, and then

He may come back a - gain._____

He may come back a - gain._____

long arpeggio

rall.

rall.

f *rall.*

ff

Dialogue
(almost Segue)

44762   Chappell

108

Nᵒ 24

PIERROT'S ENTRANCE

Cue: (Mme. DUBONNET) "Pierrot has not forgotten after all"

Chappell

№ 25

FINALE—ACT III (Ensemble)

Cue: (BOBBY) "Swell—now how about that Charleston?"

B

ENS
Life with-out us is im-poss-i-ble And de-void-of all charms.

ENS
No a-mount of i-dle gos-sip 'll Keep them out— of our arms

ENS
We're blue— with-out, Can't do— with-out, Our dreams just won't come true— with-out

ENS
That cer-tain thing called the Boy Friend.

rit. - - -

C ‰ **Moderato**

I could be hap-py with you _____ If you could be hap-py with me. _____ I'd be con- -tent-ed to live an-y-where. _____ What would I care _____

D

As long as you were there? Skies may not al-way be blue, _____ But

Broader

one thing is clear as can be, _____ I know that I could be hap-py with

rall. me. _____ *Fine*

you, My darl-ing, If you could be hap-py with me, with me.

(Segue after applause)
Chappell

№ 25a

FINAL CURTAIN

Dal 𝄋 (page 111)
al Fine

№ 26

PLAY OUT

In Bright 4

(Cymb.)

A

B

Chappell

C Moderato, not too fast *(in 4)*

accel.

f

R.H.

R.H.

rall.

a tempo

Broadly

ff

ten.

rit. *ten.*